Tuneful Graded Studies

Arranged by
DOROTHY BRADLEY

FOREWORD

The second volume of the series of Tuneful Graded Studies, which are selected from the works of standard composers, covers the most important ground in the early stages of piano tecnics:-
Formation of a good position of the hand and fingers from the simplest five - finger group to more extended positions; finger individualisation; steady, even tone in *legato* playing; finger and wrist staccato; very simple chord - playing for forearm touch; aid to time perception by gradual introduction of different note-values, rests and easy subdivisions of the beat. A few new, original studies are included.

Tempo indications are intended as general guidance to what may be expected of a young beginner. Where two sets of figures are given the first should be regarded as the lowest at which the study (after practise) should be taken for good rhythmic effect.

Volume 2 contains work which teachers will find valuable for pupils in preparation for primary and elementary examinations.

D.B.

BOSWORTH
14-15 Berners Street,
London W1T 3LJ, UK.

BOOK 2.

PRIMARY — ELEMENTARY

CONTENTS

* Autorisé par J. HAMELLE, Paris

B. & Co. Ltd 19737

TUNEFUL GRADED STUDIES

(Various Composers)

Evenness in Fingerwork, and Contractions, Right Hand

For evenness of time and tone in R.H. quavers, it is important to keep the hand steady, moulded to the keys, fingers firm at top joint, wrist free but not wobbling. Feel that the fingers are walking on the keys, so that weight is transferred from one finger to the next for perfect legato. Work from the knuckles. In bars 5, 7, and similar places, where contractions occur, the hand should be neatly closed, just enough to bring required finger over its key. L.H. must have a more singing quality of tone. Keep an absolutely steady pulse throughout.

KOHLER

Made in England

B. & Co. Ltd., 19737 Tous droits d'exécution réservés

Even Fingerwork and Contractions for Left Hand

The rules given for R.H. in No. 1 must here be applied to L.H. Great care should be taken to keep 5th finger well shaped on its key. Do not allow this finger to lie down on its side, or to play the key with a downward drive of the arm! Take hold, and *mean* every note.

Allegro moderato ♩=132

KOHLER

Tone Control, Phrasing

Let the melody flow smoothly and evenly, with gentle tone gradations and no break within the slurs. Great care should be taken with quiet entries on the half-beat, as in second (complete) bar and similar places. The small notes are very short, are played on the beat, and throw an accent upon the principal note. L.H. part must have nicely rounded tone, notes played *exactly* together.

Andante con espressione ♩=80

STAMATY

Right Hand Melody, Accompaniment
with Simple Part-Playing

The repeated note at beginning of second beat, bars 2, 4, 6, etc., must be slightly stronger than the preceding note, and the whole bar must move to the accent in following bar. Care should be taken to sustain minims in L.H., and to give them more tone than the shorter notes. They should have a warm, singing quality, and their exact tone amount should vary with the loudness or softness of the passage.

Le COUPPEY

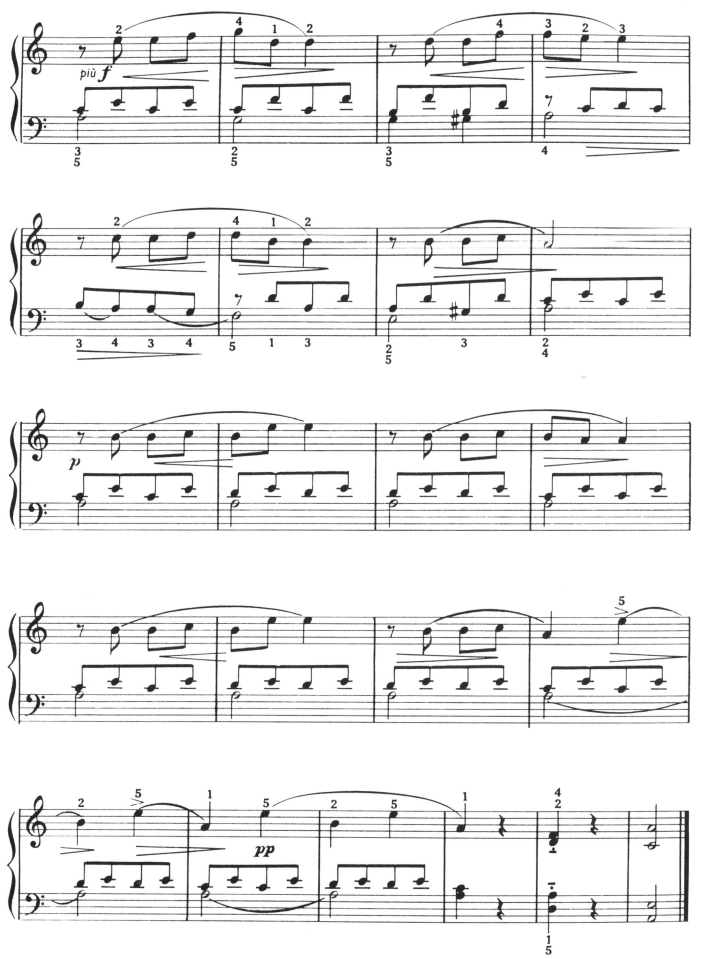

For the Weaker Fingers of Both Hands

See that the hand is well arched so that the fingers can react against the knuckles. Play in absolutely even time. In the last four bars L.H. must make small lateral adjustments to bring fingers over their new keyboard position, and at the same time fingers must always be prepared over their keys. Every finger must be in a good position for playing.

Moderato ♩ = 112-116

GURLITT

B. & Co. Ltd. 19737

Neat Fingerwork in Changing Intervals for Both Hands

Attend to the coming up as well as the going down of the keys. This is very important, otherwise the keys will be down when they are wanted again. Tone should be fairly level but not monotonous, and time very steady with clear accents. Chords should be as connected as possible, especially in the progression from weak to strong.

Allegro moderato ♩ = 132-136

LEMOINE

FINE

B. & Co. Ltd. 19737

D. C. al Fine

B. & Co. Ltd. 19737

Scale and Figure-Work for Right Hand

The staccato note on first quaver of bars 1, 5, etc., must not upset the normal accent; second quaver must enter more quietly and the whole figure must *move to the next accent*. This should be played very rhythmically with good crisp tone. In passing thumb under fingers and fingers over thumb it helps if the fingers are pointed inwards towards the middle of keyboard, with wrist slightly turned outward. See that all adjustments are neat and smooth.

Allegro moderato ♩ = 144

KOHLER

Scale and Figure-Work for Left Hand

See notes on No. 7, and apply those points to L.H. Care should be taken with the smooth progression from end of bar 13 to first note of 15. Adjust the hand quietly so that the fingers are brought over their new keys.

KOHLER

For Equalizing the Fingers
SUSTAINED MELODY

This is concerned with the holding of melody notes by the thumb, below a moving part
Avoid a down-jab of the arm in playing those thumb notes. There should be rotational help
from the forearm, but the thumb must be firm enough to take it and transmit it to the keys
without the whole hand being crushed into the thumb—and the keys   Leave a light resting
weight on the key after it is played, mould the hand and fingers over the moving notes so that
each finger has the chance to play properly.   Notice the quaver rest at beginning of bar, and be
careful to enter with upper notes exactly after a quaver value—on the half-beat.

DUVERNOY

B. & Co. Ltd. 19737

For Clearness and Smoothness in Scale and Passage Work

This brings in some of the neat curving figures prepared for in No. 9 (see last beat of bars 2, 4, 15, etc.), and it needs smoothness and good tone in R.H., with breaks only at slur ends.   L.H. chords and intervals should be crisp and bright.   Notice the changing note in middle of chords, bars 7 and 23.   Play each of these first chords firmly, then taper tone on *F sharp* in second chord.

LOESCHHORN

Allegro vivace ♩=104-108

Repeated Notes, Slurs and Staccato (R.H.)

The first of each two slurred quavers must be played by descending weight of the hand, firm finger tip carrying weight into the key: second quaver *(staccato)* must be very light, and remaining *staccato* notes, played by the same finger, lightly, with movement from the wrist only. Just give the key a little 'kick' and let it kick you back. Do not pull the hand up.

STAMATY

Moderato ♩=100-104

Repeated Notes, Slurs and Staccato (L.H.)

The same rules as for No. 11 apply here to L.H.   Make sure that 5th finger stands up for itself as the key goes down.   On no account must it be allowed to lie down on its side.   There is melody in lower notes of R.H. intervals, and these must flow in four-bar phrases.

Moderato ♩=96-100

STAMATY

Contractions and Scales for Left Hand

See that the left forearm is rotarily free, not wobbling but freely balanced, so that contractions needed to bring new fingers over their keys can easily be made. Let the lateral movements come from the wrist, forearm quiet—though it moves out with the hand for low notes. Keep the elbow perfectly quiet.

Evenness of Touch in Unison Movement

Keep the hands steady and finger tips firm; time the keys in their descent exactly together in both hands. From bar 5, care is needed not only to adjust the wrist to bring the fingers over their keys, but the fingers also must make small or larger lateral adjustments so that they will always be in position at the exact moment of playing.

B. & Co. Ltd. 19737

For the Weaker Fingers of Right Hand

Similar to No. 9, but giving more work to 4th and 5th fingers. There should be perfectly regular timing of the quavers, with firm metrical accents. First note of each bar is played only once, and it must be well sounded and fully held.

Moderato ♩=120-126

LEMOINE

ben sostenuto il basso

FINE

D.C. al Fine

B. & Co. Ltd. 19737

For the Weaker Fingers of Both Hands Alternately

This gives practice not only in finger individualization, but in quick touch changes—finger touch for the single notes, forearm touch for the chords. Shape the required fingers over their notes in each chord, and keep finger tips and knuckles firm as the keys go down. Relax when the chord has been sounded.

D. BRADLEY

B. & Co. Ltd. 19737

For Expressive Playing, Changing Intervals and Small Chords

Try for beautiful tone in this. Attend to details of *mezzo-staccato* and *legato*, and to the light
staccato notes at end of bars 5-6. Notice the melodic detail in lower L.H. notes, bars 9-12.

Staccato and Legato Thirds (Hand Touch)

The *legato* thirds are played by weight transferred from each set of fingers to the next, at the
key beds, then the *staccato* thirds are allowed to rebound with fingers at key surface; *movement
from the wrist.*

B. & Co. Ltd. 19737

Scale Passages for Both Hands

To be played very rhythmically, with tone gradations as shown, and careful treatment of the two slurred notes, bars 2, 4, 14, etc.

Allegretto ♩=92-96

LOESCHHORN

B. & Co. Ltd. 19737

Melody and Accompaniment in same Hand
against L.H. Melody

The sustained melody notes in R.H. should sing gently, so that they form a duet with L.H. melody.
Accompaniment of quavers must be smooth, quiet in comparison with the tune, and *very even* in time.

Moderato ♩=126

KOHLER

B. & Co. Ltd. 19737

Phrasing, Cantabile Touch

Try for beautiful tone in R.H. melody, and attend to phrasing exactly as marked. Bass must be steady, more subdued in tone, with well controlled accents.

Andante cantabile ♩=80-84

DUVERNOY

B. & Co. Ltd. 19737

For Rhythmic Precision in Timing Notes and Rests
(DOTTED QUAVER AND SEMIQUAVER)

Rhythm must be precise and crisp, accents not too heavy.   Be sure to give the dotted semi-quaver its full value, and play the semiquaver lightly with forward movement to the *next* note. Notice the different treatment of second part (from bar 9), where a semiquaver rest replaces the dot after the quaver, and also the quavers are themselves *staccato*.   The exact time-spot of each note must remain the same, only the *staccato* quavers must rebound when played.   The small slurs indicate smooth progression of semiquaver to following quaver, and they must *not disturb the normal accent*.   This second part should be more vigorous than first part, and in L.H., bars 9-12, the broad line of phrase must be played without break.

CZERNY

B. & Co. Ltd. 19737

Clean, Light Fingerwork for Right Hand

Keep right hand steady and play from the knuckles. Special care is needed to prepare thumb and fingers over their keys, with small lateral movements of wrist and fingers. For L.H. chords and intervals, see that the hand and fingers are rightly shaped over their keys before beginning to play. Accents, though light, should be sufficient to give a definite *two in a bar*.

Allegro animato. ♩. = 100-104

Le COUPPEY

B. & Co Ltd. 19737

Neat Fingerwork, Rhythmic Precision

Rhythm here must be well marked, the *ta-téfé tafatéfé* figures precisely timed, movement always forward to the following accent. Be careful to give the quaver rests their proper value. Taper the tone on second of each couplet of slurred notes, bars 5-6, 13, 14, L.H. and 18, 20, 26, 28, R.H., etc.

Allegro moderato ♩=96-100

Le COUPPEY

Small Broken Chords for Both Hands
FINGER INDIVIDUALIZATION

Well controlled finger movement is needed for this.   Aim for perfect smoothness, evenness of time and gentle tone gradations.

GURLITT

B. & Co. Ltd. 19737

Broken Chords and Scales

Make sure that the forearm is lightly balanced and correct fingers prepared over their keys,
and that the wrist adjusts itself laterally to bring the hand over each new note group.

CZERNY

Correct Timing and Evenness in Broken Groups

Enter softly on the first note of each R.H. group, make the *middle* note slightly more prominent,
and be sure to time the semiquaver rest correctly, so that R.H. and L.H. together will say
Tafa-téfé in each group.

BURGMULLER

B. & Co. Ltd. 19737

Chromatic Passages for Right Hand

This should sound light, merry and charming, like a quick waltz. After slow practice for accuracy, it should be taken as one beat to the bar—count 1, 2, 3, 4, to *four* bars, and make the tune, time and tone go forward to each fourth bar.

CZERNY

Contractions and Scale-Work

Exactitude with fingering is most important here. In making the contractions, see that the finger (or thumb) just used remains on its key, and use it as a pivot for the hand to close gently bringing next finger over its key. When the group has been neatly joined adjust required fingers over their new keys.

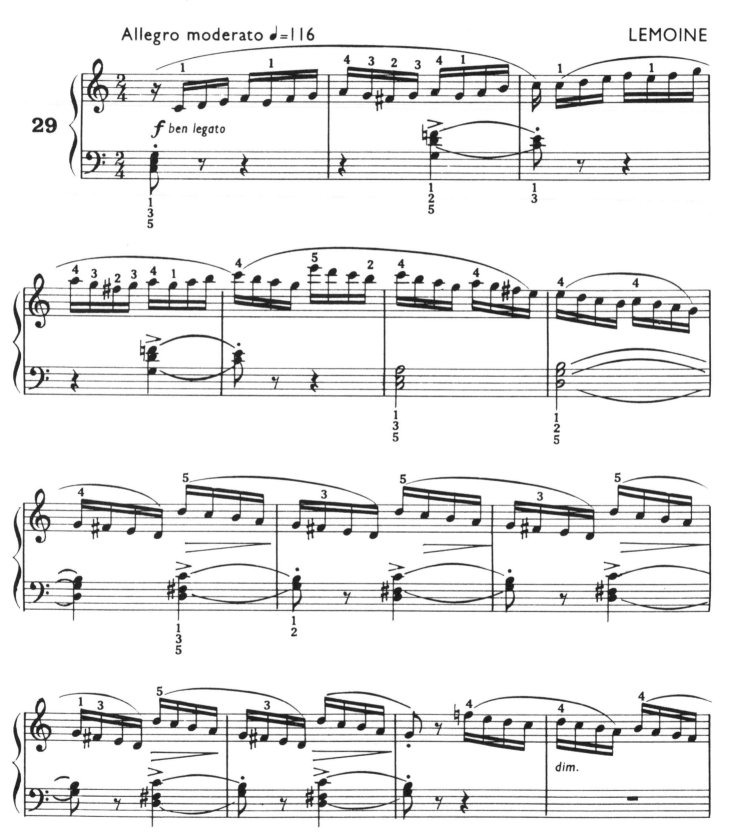

Allegro moderato ♩=116

LEMOINE

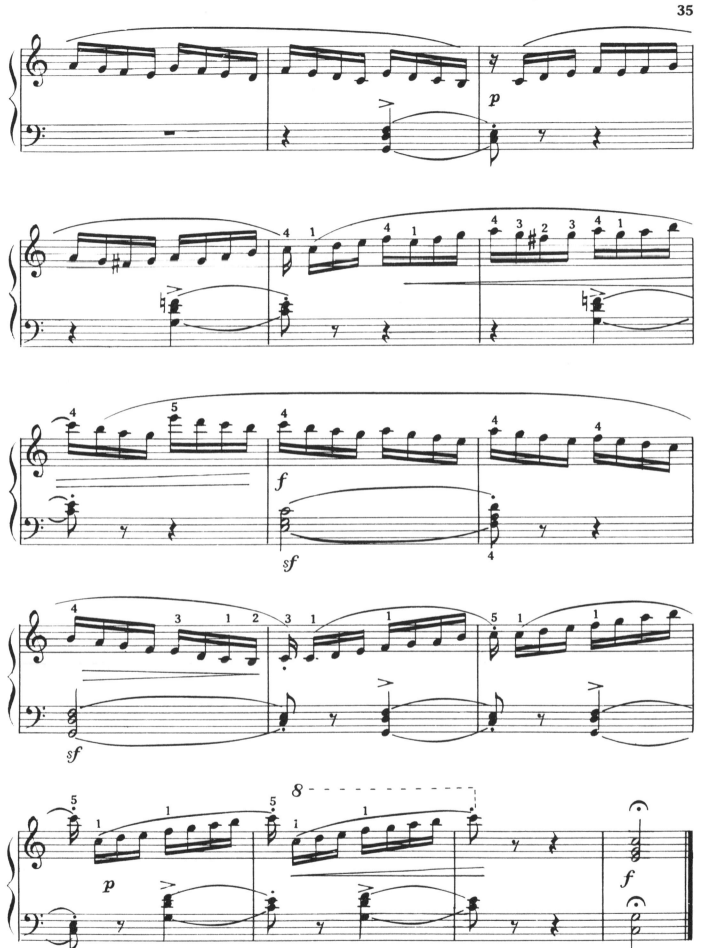

Slurred Couplets of Notes in each Hand

The first of each two slurred notes should be played by forearm descent, the finger braced to carry the key down; then the second note, tapered in tone, is played by an up movement. The resting weight from first note is transferred to the second, which should seem as if played with the tone *left over*.

Andantino ♩=104

Le COUPPEY

30

B. & Co. Ltd. 19737

D.C. al Fine

Repeated Notes with Changing Fingers for Both Hands

Play with finger movement from the knuckles, lightly poised wrist left free to vibrate, finger tips pointing to the keys. Fingers should be withdrawn slightly towards the palm of the hand when they have done their work, next finger immediately brought in contact with the key. Make first note of each group more prominent than the others, to bring out the melody. The slurs indicate *phrasing*. Use similar fingering for each four-note group throughout.

D. BRADLEY

B. & Co. Ltd. 19737

Phrasing, Right Hand Melody

The right hand melody should be played with sweet singing tone, not greatly stressed, and rising and falling within the phrase through a small range of tone. Bars 9 to 24 should be brighter, more precise, with fairly strong accents, dotted minims well played and fully held. L.H., bars 1 to 8, etc., has melodic interest in the lower notes and these should be gently marked.

LEMOINE

B. & Co. Ltd. 19737

Chromatic Passages for Right Hand

This requires very neat finger-work in R.H., with careful attention to repeated notes—middle of bars 1-4, etc.

LEMOINE

Allegretto ♩=96 (work up to 116)

Chromatic Passages for Left Hand

A lateral turning at the wrist is needed to bring L.H. over its new keys in bars 1-3, and similar places.   R.H. chords should be well sustained.

Allegretto ♩=108-112

LEMOINE

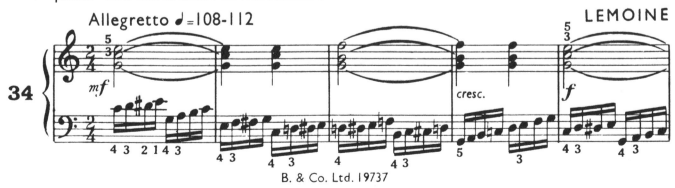

B. & Co. Ltd. 19737

Staccato Sixths, for Hand Touch

Shape the hand to the interval of a *sixth ;* play from the wrist, and keep finger and thumb firm to transmit energy to the keys.

Allegretto ♩=108-112

BERTINI

Printed by Caligraving Limited Thetford Norfolk England   B. & Co. Ltd. 19737   7/07 (62914)